CALCULATOR

FUN

Compiled by The Puzzle House
Illustrated by Barry Green

© 1991 Henderson Publishing Limited

Henderson Publishing
Woodbridge, England

ABOUT THIS BOOK

This book contains puzzles, problems, games and tricks connected with calculators. If you are a mathematical genius — or you have a lot of toes to count on — then you can still carry out most of the activities.

But this is a calculator book, and it's assumed that you've got a basic calculator to help you! You DON'T need an all-singing, headphones — included coffee making — state of the art — calculator. A standard machine with the basic functions + − × ÷ will do for most things. Ability to work memory systems will make some puzzles

easier and quicker. Scientific calculators are not needed.

Although the calculator is there to carry out the basic figurework speedily, YOU are still the major player. As well as carrying out basic calculations you've still got to grasp what's going on ... and that will involve some clear thinking, powers of observation and reasoning and a fair bit of low down cunning!

ANSWERS:

The solutions to problems appear at the back of this book.

For some questions there's only one definite solution. eg: What's the answer to $2 + 2$? (Be honest ... who turned the calculator on for that???)

For some problems there can be more than one answer eg: How can you make 4 from a sum using 2 and 2?

There's the previous example where $2 + 2 = 4$, but 2×2 also equals 4.

If there's a specific question then you'll find a specific answer. In problems such as GET TO GOAL, for example, we set you the challenge of reaching a given number using certain keys on a calculator. In some cases there will be more than one way to arrive at the answer. We provide an answer showing the way WE arrived at the answer, but if you've got there by a different route then good for you!

2 BACKCHAT

A calculator can make words as well as numbers. Work out the answers to the puzzles below, turn your calculator UPSIDE DOWN and you will have a boy's or girl's name in each case.

a) $31 \times 7 =$

b) $2 \times 3859 =$

c) $1929 \times 4 =$

d) $179 \times 3 =$

e) $1812 \div 6 =$

3 GET TO GOAL

Get to the number which is your goal using the keys given. You can use each number only once but the function keys ($+ - \times$ and $\div$) can be used as many times as you like.

Your goal is 60

Use NUMBER KEYS: 7 3 6

Use FUNCTION KEYS: $+ \times$

4 WHAT'S MY AGE?

Can you make someone confess their age without realising it? With some calculator conjuring you can!

Give the calculator to the person whose age you are going to discover. Then tell them to key in the following sequence.

STEP	1	Key in their age
STEP	2	×5
STEP	3	+5
STEP	4	×2
STEP	5	+5
STEP	6	×10

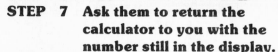

STEP 7 Ask them to return the calculator to you with the number still in the display.

STEP 8 −87 from the number in the display.

STEP 9 Remove the last two digits from the number left.

STEP 10 This is their age which you have magically discovered!

5 | ROUTE 100

Use your calculator to help you take the
route from A to B. Pass through the boxes,
adding as you go, so that you reach a total
of exactly 100.

6 | WHAT'S NEXT?

The numbers are arranged in a certain
sequence.
Can you work out what the pattern is, and
then calculate the next TWO numbers?

32   64   128 ___ ___

7 WORDSWORTH

O N E	= 3 6	T E N	= 3 3
B O N E	= 5 6	O B O E	= 5 3
T O N E	= 4 2		

In this code puzzle, each of the letters B, E, N, O and T has been given a numerical value.

The number totals are reached by adding together individual values in each word.

For example in O N E = 36, this could be made up of 0 = 30 + N = 4 + E = 2. (It COULD be but you'll find that it isn't!)

Can you crack the code to work out the value of each letter, then calculate the total value of the word **B O N N E T ?**

8 GET TO GOAL

Get to the number which is your goal using the keys given. You can use each number only once but the function keys (+ – × and ÷) can be used as many times as you like.

Your goal is 63
Use NUMBER KEYS: 4 2 9 9
Use FUNCTION KEYS: × –

9 MAGIC SQUARES

A magic square adds up to the same total whether you read it across, down or diagonally. Using your calculator complete the magic squares below. We have given you an example to set you on your way.

10	15	8
9	11	13
14	7	12

Now complete these . . . . .

	1	
	5	
4	9	

7		11
	8	
5		

6		4
	7	
		8

10 ON TARGET

Using only these keys make the TARGET number. You can use numbers and function keys as many times as you like.

NUMBER KEYS: 2 3 8
FUNCTION KEYS: × +

Example: TARGET: 4
         SOLUTION: 2 + 2 = 4

Using the same NUMBER KEYS and FUNCTION KEYS try to reach these TARGETS

a) 5   b) 11   c) 16   d) 19   e) 48

11 STEPPING STONES

Move along the route deciding what number to add or subtract to reach the number on the next stepping stone. The first couple are done to start you on your way.

START

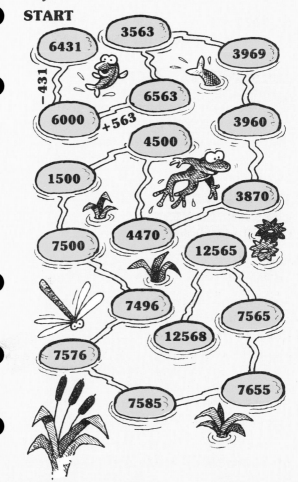

12 BACKCHAT

A calculator can make words as well as numbers. Work out the answers to the puzzles below, turn your calculator UPSIDE DOWN and make a word in each case.

a) 1911×3 c) $3651 + 1986$
b) $49612 + 5766$ d) $29611 + 8207$

13 GET TO GOAL

Get to the number which is your goal using the keys given. You can use each number only once but the function keys ($+ 1 \times$ and $\div$) can be used as many times as you like.

Your goal is 2
Use NUMBER KEYS: 9 5 1
Use FUNCTION KEYS: $+$ $\div$

14 MAKE A NUMBER

Make a number appear without using any of the digits in that number.
Use just $+ 1$ and $=$ keys
Example — Make 26
$7 + 7 + 7 + 7 = 28$. You can't take away 2 as this appears in the number.
So add another 7, $+ 7 = 35$
Take away 9, $- 9 = 26$

a) Make 37 c) Make 24 e) Make 41
b) Make 35 d) Make 39

15 WHAT'S NEXT?

The numbers are arranged in a certain sequence. Can you work out what the pattern is, and then calculate the next TWO numbers?

13 17 34 38 76 80 ____ ____

16 NAILED

Ivor Hammer has a box full of nails which contains exactly 3500 nails. He's also got seven packets of 250 nails, two packets of 300 nails, twelve packets of 75 nails and sixteen packets of 80 nails. How many packets of nails can he get into the box?

Use the chart to crack the calculator code.
Work out each puzzle below using your
calculator. Each answer can be checked
against the chart to give you a letter. Put
all the letters together to find the name of a
famous landmark. There are three for you
to work out altogether.

For example: No 1

57 ÷ 3 = 19
Check the chart
19 stands for letter E which is
the first letter of the
landmark.

**Now work out the rest of the puzzles
to crack the code.**

A	B	C	D	E	F	G
18	14	10	13	19	22	31

H	I	J	K	L	M	N
16	88	24	33	30	26	17

O	P	Q	R	S	T	U
8	41	38	42	7	23	44

V	W	X	Y	Z
39	6	12	43	51

1 57÷3 / 64+24 / 66÷3 / 31−9 /
   456−437 / 3×10

   138÷6 / 800÷100 / 12−6 /
   930−911 / 89−47

ANSWER: _____

2 19 + 4 / 128 ÷ 16 / 104 − 98 / 361 ÷ 19
  126 ÷ 3

  96 ÷ 12 / 11 × 2

  120 ÷ 4 / 373 − 365 / 408 ÷ 24 /
  644 − 631 / 800 ÷ 100 / 306 ÷ 18

  ANSWER: _____

3 96 − 89 / 736 ÷ 32 / 9 × 2 / 529 ÷ 23 /
  11 × 4 / 388 − 369

  34 − 26 / 596 − 574

  6 × 5 / 399 − 311 / 196 ÷ 14 /
  784 − 765 / 23 + 19 / 276 ÷ 12 /
  188 − 145

  ANSWER: _____

18 CALCULATOR TRAIL

With the help of your calculator, start on the top row with the circled number, and take a trail through the number square so that the numbers you meet add up to 100 exactly. You can move down, sideways and diagonally.

19 GET TO GOAL

Get to the number which is your goal using the keys given. You can use each number only once but the function keys (+ − × and ÷) can be used as many times as you like.

Your goal is 219
Use NUMBER KEYS: 100 9 2 1
Use FUNCTION KEYS: + ×

20 SUM PROBLEM

Replace the listed numbers in the frame so that each row across and each column down totals the target number.

TARGET: 21
USE THESE NUMBERS:
1 3 4 4 4 5 5 6 7 8

8	3	5	4	1
2				7
1				3
3				4
7	1	5	2	6

21 ON TARGET

More TARGET practice!
See number 10 for instructions and aim to hit the TARGETS below!
NUMBER KEYS: 9 3 6
FUNCTION KEYS: + ÷ − ×

a) 2
b) 18
c) 21
d) 45
e) 162

22 BACKCHAT

A calculator can make words as well as numbers. Work out the answers to the puzzles below, turn your calculator UPSIDE DOWN and you will have words with a gardening link. We give you a clue in each case.

a) **76 × 4** (Garden tool)
b) **876 × 4** (Used for watering)
c) **1421 × 5** (Dig this!)
d) **395 + 212** (Chopped wood makes this)
e) **369 + 341** (If you find this in the garden, you're rich!)

23 GET TO GOAL

Get to the number which is your goal using the keys given. You can use each number only once, but the function keys (+ − × ÷) can be used as many times as you like.

Your goal is 808

Use NUMBER KEYS: 50 7 9 3 5
Use FUNCTION KEYS: + ×

24 QUIZZUMS

A quiz and a sum in one! Use your calculator to help you find the answer!

1 James Bond's Secret Agent number × degrees Fahrenheit which is the same as 100 degrees Centigrade (i.e. boiling point of water)

   ANSWER: _____

2 Metres in the race where Sebastian Coe won Olympic gold in Moscow and Los Angeles + the number of each animal put in the Ark by Noah × Blind Mice in the Nursery Rhyme

   ANSWER: _____

3 BBC Radio Station which had its 1st birthday in August 1991 × colours in the French flag × days in a fortnight

   ANSWER: _____

4 Pennies in a £1 × Chancellor of the Exchequer's house in Downing Street × emergency telephone number

   ANSWER: _____

5 Time of the Train from Manchester in the TV programme + telephone code for inner London + telephone code for outer London

   ANSWER: _____

25 | MAGIC SQUARES

A magic square adds up to the same total whether you read it across, down or diagonally. Using your calculator complete the magic squares below, with the number 1 to 16 in each square.

26 | WHAT'S NEXT?

The numbers are arranged in a certain sequence. Can you work out what the pattern is, and then calculate the next TWO numbers?

33 11 66 22 132 44 ___ ___

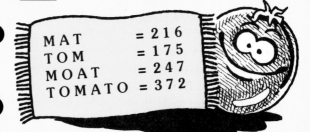

MAT = 216
TOM = 175
MOAT = 247
TOMATO = 372

In this code puzzle, each of the letters A, M, O and T has been given a numerical value.

The number totals are reached by adding together individual values in each word.

For example in M A T = 2 1 6, this could be made up of

M = 180 + A = 20 + T = 16.

(It COULD be but it isn't!)

Can you calculate the value of the FOUR letters so that all the totals are correct?

28 GET TO GOAL

Get to the number which is your goal using the keys given. You can use each number only once but the function keys
(+ − × and ÷) can be used as many times as you like.

Your goal is 357

Use NUMBER KEYS: 50 1 7
Use FUNCTION KEYS: × +

29 ALL SQUARE

Move from square to square up, down, across and backwards but NOT diagonally. Using your calculator to help you, find a way from the shaded square to the circled square so that the numbers you pass through add up to 150.

START

			30	5	6	7	39	40	
			21	2	40	9	70	54	
			70	8	17	3	27	37	
			7	3	19	6	49	41	
			80	60	50	4	37	7	
90	20	19	31	5	4	7	3	28	19
27	41	70	35	1	38	71	39	31	21
1	8	9	1	3	17	23	29	10	20
2	34	70	40	30	17	20	18	19	15
5	8	3	19	10	19	28	31	27	30
27	31	7	15	20	15	29			
40	21	4	30	36	3	①			
31	29	9	3	1	2	20			

FINISH

30 INCALCULABLE!

Here's a crazy-looking calculator! Yet there's a logical explanation why the keys are arranged in this way. You don't need to work out any calculator sums to arrive at the solution ... but you do need to study the numbers and the function keys. Any more clues and we would be spelling out the answer for you.

Can you work out the reason for this arrangement?

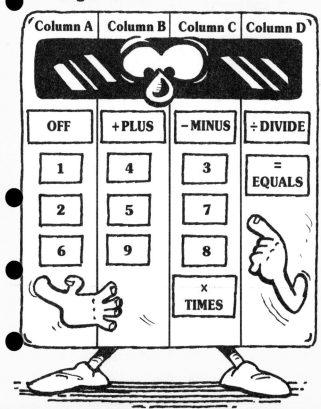

Column A	Column B	Column C	Column D
OFF	+PLUS	−MINUS	÷DIVIDE
1	4	3	= EQUALS
2	5	7	
6	9	8	
		× TIMES	

31 FIVERS

Here's a bunch of fives. Count the fives,
multiplying the total each time you count a
number. (5 × 5 = 25. 25 × 5 = 125 and so on)
What's the final total?

32 PICK A CARD!

Here's a trick where you use your trusty
calculator to identify a playing card!

1   **Use a standard pack of playing
    cards. Ask a friend to take out any
    card. They can see what the card is
    but you can't.**
2   **Give your friend a calculator and
    ask him or her to multiply the
    number of the card by 10. An ace
    counts as 1, jack as 11, queen as
    12 and king as 13.**

3 Multiply answer × 3.

4 Now add 1 for a club, 2 for a heart, 3 for a spade and 4 for a diamond.

5 Your friend doubles the number then gives you the calculator with the number showing on the display.

6 You divide the number by 2. The last digit of your answer will reveal the suit . . . 1 for a club, and so on as in stage 4 of the trick.

7 The first digits are ÷ 3. That will reveal the number of the card. Magic!

For example: King of hearts. Worth 13.
$13 \times 10 = 130$.
$130 \times 3 = 390$.
$390 + 2$ (for hearts) $= 392$.
$392 \times 2 = 784$.
$784 \div 2 = 392$. The last digit stands for the suit . . . 2 for hearts. 39 is divided by 3 to give 13 . . . the value of the king.

33 BACKCHAT

A calculator can make words as well as numbers. Work out the answers to the puzzles below, turn your calculator UPSIDE DOWN and you will have a word in each case.

a) **Could be a cold house!**

   $0.0123 + 0.0668 =$

b) **Bad news for cyclists and walkers!**

   $5632 + 2082 =$

c) **Found on the beach**

   $66666 + 10679 =$

d) **A form of greeting**

   $0.8968 - 0.1234 =$

e) **Could be found in a church or a school**

   $6311 + 1427 =$

34 GET TO GOAL

Get to the number which is your goal using the keys given. You can use each number only once but the function keys
(+ − × and ÷) can be used as many times as you like.

Your goal is 742

Use NUMBER KEYS: 100 6 7
Use FUNCTION KEYS: + ×

35 ROUTE 100

Use your calculator to help you take the route from A to B. Pass through the boxes, adding as you go, so that you reach a total of exactly 100.

		A	
21	20	28	16
	27	29	12
11	22	18	25
	26	15	6
14	9	17	19
		B	

36 WHAT'S NEXT?

The numbers are arranged in a certain sequence. Can you work out what the pattern is, and then calculate the next two numbers?

3000 2832 2664 2496 ____ ____

37 LOST IN THE MAZE

Start with a total of 50000. As you move along the paths take away all the numbers that you cross from your starter total. Which path will leave you the highest number when you come out of the maze?

Each path goes through EIGHT NUMBERS

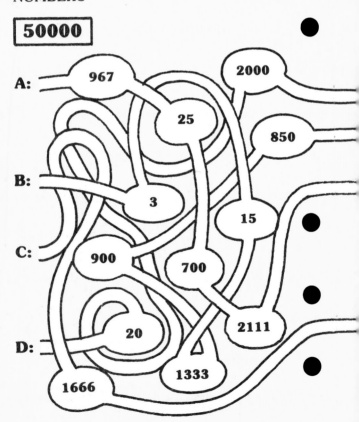

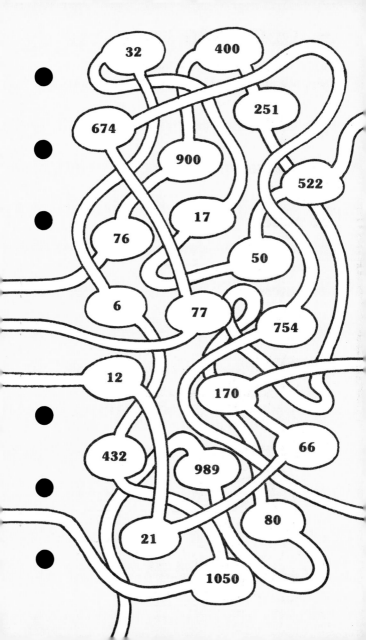

A quiz and a sum in one! Find the answers to the puzzles below!

1   Snow White's Dwarfs × Days Michael Palin, Willy Fog and Phileas Fogg travelled around the world

ANSWER: _____

2   Disney's Dalmatians × days in 1991

ANSWER: _____

3   Year England won the World Cup – year of the Battle of Hastings

ANSWER: _____

4   Hours in a day × days in February in 1988

ANSWER: _____

5   Enid Blyton's Famous gang of children × numbers of brothers Princess Anne has × players in a soccer team

ANSWER: _____

39 THINK OF A NUMBER

Calculator conjuring to astound your friends! Ask a pal to think of a number up to FIVE digits and put it on the calculator display without your seeing it.
Then get your friend to do the following:

1) × number by 5
2) + 25
3) × 5
4) + 35
5) × 4
6) Return the calculator to you with the final figure still on the display.

Now it's up to you. Subtract 640 from the total. Remove the last TWO digits and you will have the number that your friend thought of!

40 DIVIDERS

Greedy Greg has a box of sweets that he's tipped out on the floor. He tries dividing the sweets into groups. He finds that in groups of THREE there's one sweet left over. The same happens when the sweets are divided into groups of FOUR, FIVE and SIX. But when Greg splits the sweets into groups of SEVEN there are none left over.

How many sweets did he start with?

41 BACKCHAT

A calculator can make words as well as numbers. Work out the answers to the puzzles below, turn your calculator upside down and you will have a word . . . and all words have a connection with animals.

a) **Nickname for a lion.**

$0.18 + 0.19 =$

b) **What noise do turkeys make?**

$155699 + 223107 =$

c) **Birds which were once used as traditional Christmas fare.**

$47681 - 12345 =$

d) **An insect which lives in a colony.**

$169 \times 2 =$

e) **Place where wild animals are kept so people in cities can see them.**

$0.45 - 0.43 =$

42 GET TO GOAL

Get to the number which is your goal using the keys given. You can use each number only once but the function keys (+ − × ÷) can be used as many times as you like.

Your goal is 474

Use NUMBER KEYS: 75 5 2 3 9 6
Use FUNCTION KEYS: + − × ÷

43 MAGIC SQUARE

A magic square adds up to the same total whether you read it across, down or diagonally. Using your calculator complete the magic square below. You will need to use all the numbers between 1 and 25.

		1		15
17	5	7	14	
4		13	20	22
	12	19	21	3
11	18			

44 ODD ONE OUT

Solve the puzzles below and discover which solution is the ODD ONE OUT

a) 965 + 146

b) 707 × 11

c) 2403 × 4

d) 3698 + 1857

45 CALCULATOR TRAIL

With the help of your calculator, start on the top row with the circled number, and take a trail through the number square so that the numbers you meet add up to 100 exactly. You can move down, sideways and diagonally.

18	5	23	30	(21)	52
10	19	1	40	18	30
20	7	9	1	60	11
2	5	15	3	40	12
2	20	13	12	21	30
50	12	50	10	14	14

46 SUM PROBLEM

Replace the listed numbers in the frame so that each row across and column down totals the target number.

TARGET: 65   USE THESE NUMBERS:

9	3	22		
2	21			8
25			7	1
		6	5	24
	10	4	23	

11 12 13 14 15
16 17 18 19 20

47 DODGER!

Here's a calculator game where you have to dodge the given number. It's great fun to play with a friend but you can play on your own.

Start with 0 and taking turns add one digit key 1-9 each time and avoid the given number. Use just the + and − keys.

Try to DODGE

a) 14

b) 17

c) 22

d) 32

e) 19

When you're good at DODGER try this variation. Throw a dice to decide on the number to be used but you choose whether to use the + − × or ÷ key.

Now find some DODGER numbers of your own.

48 GET TO GOAL

Get to the number which is your goal using the keys given. You can use each number only once but the function keys (+ − × ÷) can be used as many times as you like.

Your goal is 214

USE NUMBER KEYS: 25 6 6 4 3 10
USE FUNCTION KEYS: + − × ÷

49 WHAT'S NEXT?

The numbers are arranged in a certain sequence. Can you work out what the pattern is, and then calculate the next two numbers?

25 50 150 600 3000 ___ ___

50 MAGIC SQUARE

A magic square adds up to the same total whether you read it across, down or diagonally. Complete the magic square below in which the total is 195.

45			9	27
24			63	
3	21	39		75
	15			54
	69	12	30	

51 SEVEN UP

How many 7's are there in the picture? For each number you count, multiply by 7 (7 × 7 = 49. 49 × 7 = 343, and so on.)
What's the total?

52 BACKCHAT

A calculator can make words as well as numbers. Work out the answers to the puzzles below, turn your calculator upside down and discover the words.

a) **You do this when something goes missing.**

   7 × 501 =

b) **Very large**

   103 × 6 =

c) **Person who is in charge**

   1377 × 4 =

53 GET TO GOAL

Get to the number which is your goal using the keys given. You can use each number only once but the function keys (+ − × ÷) can be used as many times as you like.

Your goal is 234

Use NUMBER KEYS: 75 4 3 3

Use FUNCTION KEYS: + × −

54 CODEBUSTER

Use the chart to crack the calculator code. Work out each puzzle using your calculator. Each answer can be checked against the chart to give you a letter. Put all the letters together to find the name of a famous person.

There are four for you to work out altogether.

For example: No 1

$224 \div 56 = 4$
Check the chart
4 stands for the letter M so the person's name begins with M.

Now work out the rest of the puzzles to
crack the code.

A B C D E F G
1 7 8 11 3 13 5

H I J K L M N
26 15 2 9 10 4 14

O P Q R S T U
6 12 21 22 23 24 25

V W X Y Z
19 18 17 20 16

1   224 ÷ 56 / 999 − 998 / 121 ÷ 11 /
853 − 847 / 294 ÷ 21 / 7 × 2 / 85 ÷ 85

ANSWER: _____

2   504 ÷ 42 / 999 ÷ 999 / 300 ÷ 12 /
100 − 90 /

25 ÷ 5 / 63 − 62 / 276 ÷ 12 / 888 − 880
/ 55 − 49 / 75 − 60 / 995 − 990 /
728 ÷ 52 / 66 − 63

ANSWER: _____

3   2 × 1 / 76 − 70 / 956 − 930 / 448 ÷ 32 /
300 ÷ 75 / 721 − 720 / 912 ÷ 456 /
576 ÷ 96 / 352 ÷ 16

ANSWER: _____

55 CALCULATOR WORD SEARCH

Work out the answers to the number puzzles below then seek out the answer in the word search square. Words are in straight lines and read across, backwards, up, down or diagonally. You can use letters more than once but you don't have to use them all.

a) $1512 \div 24 =$

b) $96 \div 12 =$

c) $988 - 987 =$

d) $448 \div 64 =$

e) $1056 \div 96 =$

f) $866 - 853 =$

g) $261 \div 87 =$

h) $396 \div 99 =$

i) $6356 - 6341 =$

j) $784 \div 56 =$

k) $1760 \div 88 =$

l) $13572 \div 754 =$

m) $6201 \div 689 =$

n) $965 \div 193 =$

o) $11374 \div 5687 =$

S	O	T	W	E	F	N	F	T	N
N	I	E	N	O	N	Y	I	Y	I
N	N	X	U	E	T	I	V	N	N
E	M	R	T	N	V	N	E	E	E
E	I	O	E	Y	E	E	E	I	O
T	L	W	L	E	T	T	L	S	T
R	T	T	T	H	R	H	N	E	H
U	T	F	G	I	R	H	R	V	G
O	I	I	H	I	L	L	T	E	I
F	E	T	I	O	N	S	O	N	E

56 ROUTE 100

Use your calculator to help you take the route from A to B. Pass through the boxes, adding as you go, so that you reach a total of exactly 100.

57 WHAT'S NEXT?

The numbers are arranged in a certain sequence. Can you work out what the pattern is, and then calculate the next TWO numbers?

1 3 7 15 31 63 ___ ___

58 QUIZZUMS

A quiz and a sum in one! Work out the answers below!

1 English kings called Henry × Days of Christmas in the famous carol × legs of an octopus

   ANSWER: _____

2 A dozen × hours in a day × letters in the alphabet

   ANSWER: _____

3 Age when you can vote in the UK × age you can leave school ÷ leaves in a lucky clover

   ANSWER: _____

4 Cards in a pack without jokers × total chess pieces on the board at start of play ÷ legs on a spider

   ANSWER: _____

5 Highest score with three darts when the bull's eye is not hit − total players on a soccer pitch at the start of play × players left in the semi final of a singles tennis tournament

   ANSWER: _____

59 TEN TEST

Numbers have been replaced by symbols. There are EIGHT different symbols used, standing in place of the tens from 10 to 80. The numbers at the end of the rows and columns are worked out by adding together the values of the symbols. Can you crack the code and work out what each symbol is worth?

☺	▲	▣	☺	▲	130
★	◎	◗	✖	◎	230
✿	◎	☺	✿	★	190
▣	▲	✿	◗	▲	240
☺	▣	◎	✿	☺	150
170	150	210	280	130	

☺ = ___ ▲ = ___ ▣ = ___ ★ = ___

◎ = ___ ◗ = ___ ✖ = ___ ✿ = ___

60 BACKCHAT

A calculator can make words as well as numbers. Work out the answers to the puzzles below, turn your calculator UPSIDE DOWN and you will have a word in each case.

a) $888.5 \times 8 =$

b) $13527 \div 3 =$

c) $25101776 \div 632 =$

d) $643 \times 5 =$

e) $115374 \div 123 =$

61 GET TO GOAL

Get to the number which is your goal using the keys given. You can use each number only once but the function keys ($+$ $-$ $\times$ $\div$) can be used as many times as you like.

Your goal is 211

Use NUMBER KEYS: 75 3 6 8
Use FUNCTION KEYS: $\times$ $-$

ANSWERS

5. Route 100

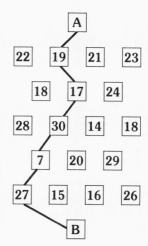

2. Backchat
a Liz / 217.
b Bill / 7718.
c Gill / 7716.
d Les / 537.
e Zoe / 302.

3. Get to Goal
7 + 3 = 10   10 × 6 = 60

6. What's Next?
256 512. Each
number is doubled.

7. Wordsworth
B = 20, E = 15, N = 12, O = 9, T = 6.
Bonnet = 74. In letters, the only difference
between BONE and ONE is the B. Take away
the value of ONE from BONE to arrive at B's
value. The same applies for the letter T
(TONE – ONE). Take TEN from value of TONE
to arrive at 0. Knowing the values of O and B
you can work out what E is worth in the word
OBOE. Knowing O and E you can do the same
with ONE to find the value of N.

8. Get To Goal
4 × 2 = 8.   8 × 9 = 72.
72 – 9 = 63.

9. Magic Squares

8	1	6
3	5	7
4	9	2

7	6	11
12	8	4
5	10	9

6	11	4
5	7	9
10	3	8

11. Stepping Stones
− 431. + 563. − 3000.
+ 406. − 9. − 90.
+ 600. + 30. − 3000.
+ 6000. − 4. + 80.
+ 9. + 70. − 90.
+ 5000. + 3.

12. Backchat
a Eels / 5733.
b Bless / 55 378.
c Legs / 5637.
d Bible / 37818.

13. Get To Goal
9 + 1 = 10. 10 ÷ 5 = 2.

15. What's Next?
160. 164.
4 is added to the first number to make the second number, then the second number is doubled.

16. Nailed
None. The box is already full of nails!

17. Codebuster
1 Eiffel Tower.
2 Tower Of London.
3 Statue Of Liberty.

18. Calculator Trail
19 + 12 + 16 + 9
+ 27 + 17

19. Get To Goal
100 + 9 = 109.
109 × 2 + 218.
218 + 1 = 219.

20. Sum Problem

8	3	5	4	1
2	5	4	3	7
1	4	6	7	3
3	8	1	5	4
7	1	5	2	6

22. Backchat
a Hoe / 304.
b Hose / 3504.
c Soil / 7105.
d Log / 607.
e Oil / 710.

23. Get To Goal
9 + 7 = 16.
16 × 50 = 800.
800 + 3 + 5 = 808.

24. Quizzums
1 007 × 212 = 1484.
2 (1500 + 2) × 3 = 4506.
3 5 × 3 × 14 = 210.
4 100 × 11 × 999 = 1098900.
5 815 + 071 + 081 = 967.

25. Magic Squares

1	12	8	13
14	7	11	2
15	6	10	3
4	9	5	16

16	2	3	13
5	10	11	8
9	6	7	12
4	15	14	1

16	3	2	13
5	10	11	8
9	6	7	12
4	15	14	1

26. What's Next?

264. 88.

Pattern is ÷ first
number by 3, then ×
second number by 6.

27. Wordsworth

A = 72. M = 50. O = 31. T = 94.

Difference between TOM and MOAT is the
letter A. So take away the value of TOM from
MOAT to find the value of A. In the same way,
take value of MAT from MOAT to find the value
of O. If you put the letters together in the words
TOM and MOAT, you'll find they are the same
as in TOMATO but there's an extra M. Add up
the values of TOM and MOAT then take
TOMATO away to get the value of M.

T appears in three-letter words where you now
know the values of the other two letters.

28. Get To Goal

50 + 1 = 51.

51 × 7 = 357.

29. All Square

one route can be:

30	5	6	7	39	40
21	2	40	9	70	54
70	8	17	3	27	37
7	3	19	6	49	41
80	60	50	4	37	7

START points to the fourth row (7 3 19 6 49 41).

90	20	19	31	5	4	7	3	28	19
27	41	70	35	1	38	71	39	31	21
1	8	9	1	3	17	23	29	10	20
2	34	70	40	30	17	20	18	19	15
5	8	3	19	10	19	28	31	27	30
27	31	7	15	20	15	29			
40	21	4	30	36	3	1			
31	29	9	3	1	2	20			

FINISH

30. Incalculable!
Arranged according to number of letters when spelt out as words. Column A has three letters, column B has four, column C has five and column D has six.

31. Fivers
48828125

33. Backchat
a Igloo / 00791.
b Hill / 7714.
c Shell / 77345.
d Hello / 0.77345.
e Bell / 7738.

34. Get To Goal
$100 + 6 = 106$.
$106 \times 7 = 742$.

35. Route 100

37. Lost In The Maze
A: 928. B: 394.
C: 1225. D: 284.

38. Quizzums
1 $80 \times 7 = 560$.
2 $365 \times 101 = 36865$.
3 $1966 - 1066 = 900$.
4 $24 \times 29 = 696$.
5 $5 \times 3 \times 11 = 165$.

40. Dividers
301.

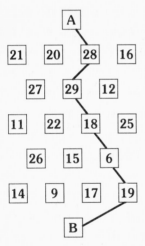

36. What's Next?
2328. 2160.
– 168 from previous number.

41. Backchat
a Leo / 0.37.
b Gobble / 378806.
c Geese / 35336.
d Bee / 238.
e Zoo / 0.02.

42. Get To Goal
$75 \times 6 = 450.$
$3 \times 9 = 27.$
$450 + 27 = 477.$
$477 - 5 = 472.$
$472 + 2 = 474.$

43. Magic Square

17	24	1	8	15
23	5	7	14	16
4	6	13	20	22
10	12	19	21	3
11	18	25	2	9

44. Odd One Out
a) 1111 b) 7777
c) 9612 d) 5555
c) is the Odd One Out

45. Calculator Trail
21 40 9 5 13 12.

46. Sum Problem

9	3	22	16	15
2	21	20	14	8
25	19	13	7	1
18	12	6	5	24
11	10	4	23	17

48. Get To Goal
$25 - 4 = 21.$
$21 \times 10 = 210.$
$6 \div 6 = 1. \ 1 + 3 = 4.$
$210 + 4 = 214.$

49. What's Next?
1800. 126000.
First number × 2.
Second × 3 and so on.

50. Magic Square

45	48	66	9	27
24	42	60	63	6
3	21	39	57	75
72	15	18	36	54
51	69	12	30	33

51. 7 Up
40353607

52. Backchat
a Lose / 3507.
b Big / 618.
c Boss / 5508.

53. Get To Goal
$75 + 4 = 79.$
$79 \times 3 = 237.$
$237 - 3 = 234.$

54. Codebuster
1 Madonna.
2 Paul Gascoigne.
3 John Major.

55. Calculator Word Search
a Sixty Three, b Eight, c One, d Seven,
e Eleven, f Thirteen, g Three, h Four, i Fifteen,
j Fourteen, k Twenty, l Eighteen, m Nine,
n Five, o Two.

56. Route 100

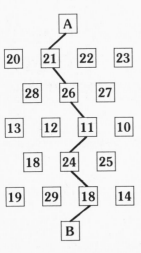

57. What's Next?
127. 255.
The next number in
value is added to each
number in the pattern.
1 + 2 = 3. 3 + 4 = 7.
7 + 8 = 15 and so on.

58. Quizzums
1 8 × 12 × 8 = 768.
2 12 × 24 × 26 = 7488.
3 (18 × 16) ÷ 4 = 72.
4 (52 × 32) ÷ 8 = 208.
5 (180 − 22) × 4 = 632.

59. Ten Test
☺ = 10 ▲ = 30 ✕ = 50
★ = 40 ◎ = 20 ☾ = 70
❦ = 80 ✿ = 60

60. Backchat
a Boil / 7108.
b Gosh / 4509.
c Bilge / 39718.
d Size / 3215.
e Beg / 938.

61. Get To Goal
75 × 3 = 225.
225 − 8 = 217.
217 − 6 = 211.